My Scar is Beautiful

By Caryn Shender

Illustrated by Zulfiqar Soleh

HP | Harpenela Publishing

My Scar is Beautiful by Caryn Shender

Copyright © Harpenela Publishing 2021

Second Edition, 2022
ISBN: 978-0-578-35354-8
Maryland, United States
Published by Harpenela Publishing 2021

Illustrated by Zulfiqar Soleh
Edited by Laurie Pickei

www.MyScarisBeautifulBook.com

DEDICATION

To my daughter Elaina: I am proud of and inspired by you every day. I love you!

To anyone with a special scar, no matter how it came to be.

To all the cardiac kids who left us too soon. May their memory be a blessing.

To doctors Scott Freedman, M.D., Darren Klugman, M.D., and cardiac surgeon Bret Mettler, M.D. Elaina is alive and celebrating her scar because of you. We are forever grateful.

_____ scar is BEAUTIFUL.

Fill In Your Name

My beautiful scar reminds me...

People care about me.
Doctors, nurses, and my family all fought for me.

I am worthy and I am loved.

Some people wear jewelry.

I wear my scar proudly like a badge of honor.

My beautiful scar reminds me...

I can survive any storm that comes my way.

I am brave, resilient, and strong.

One must fight in a battle to earn the title of warrior.

I am a warrior.

My beautiful scar reminds me...

People may try to make me feel embarrassed or ashamed of my scar. I know I did my best and it shows my bravery and courage.

I am proud of myself and my scar.

People may make up wild stories and think my scar is from a shark bite, a lightning bolt, or even a sword fight.

The truth is cooler than anything
that can be imagined.

My beautiful scar reminds me...

During difficult times, I can look at my scar and know
that I have fought through my hardest days.

I am a fighter and a survivor.

Many people have scars on their bodies, sometimes more than one. Some are thick or thin, flat or raised, straight or crooked. Like snowflakes, no two scars are the same.

I am both one-of-a-kind and not alone.

My beautiful scar reminds me...

Being different is good!
My experience sets me apart.

I have a unique story to tell.

Some people may not get it.
They may be quick to judge, think I don't look "normal,"
or might even point and stare.

I can help others understand by telling them how I got my scar.

My beautiful scar reminds me...

I can do anything I set my mind to. My scar shows
what I have overcome and is proof of my survival.

My scar is part of me, but does not define me.
It does not limit what I can do nor who I will become.

Everyone faces challenges. Mine were scary and life changing and left a beautiful mark that shows I am tough.

I love my scar.

It is my special gift and has helped shape who I am.

My beautiful scar reminds me...

My body's ability to heal is magical.

I am a real-life superhero!

MY BEAUTIFUL SCAR REMINDS ME...

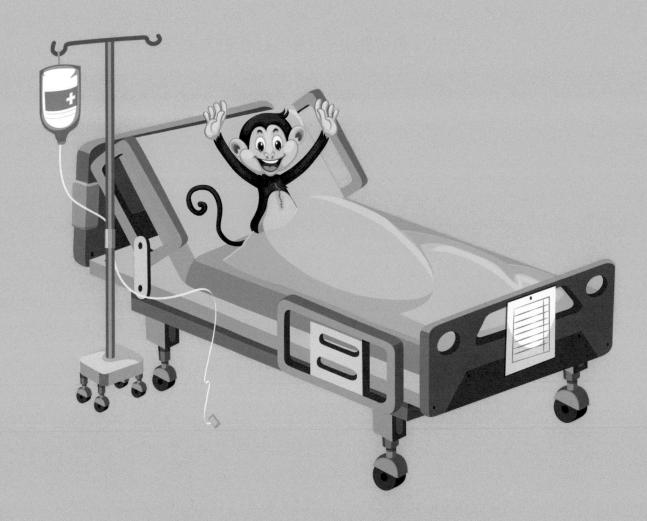

Life is precious. I am alive.

I am grateful for my scar.

My scar is BEAUTIFUL!

Inspirational Quotes

"Scars are not signs of weakness, they are signs of survival and endurance."
- Author Rodney A. Winters

"My scars tell a story. They are a reminder of times when life tried to break me, but failed. They are markings of where the structure of my character was welded." - Author Steve Maraboli

"From every wound there is a scar, and every scar tells a story. A story that says, 'I survived.'" - Fr. Craig Scott

"Scars show toughness: that you've been through it, and you're still standing."
- Actor Theo Rossi

"Makeup artists are always trying to cover it up, but I don't want to hide it.
I wouldn't be here today if I didn't have this scar." - Actor Catherine Zeta-Jones

"If I died without scars that just means I did nothing worth fighting for. "
- NFL Quarterback Joe Burrow

About the Author:

Caryn Shender is a proud mom, author, certified pediatric sleep specialist, and founder of Sleep Tight Tonight. Her daughter was born with ALCAPA, an extremely rare congenital heart defect (CHD) and is the inspiration behind My Scar is Beautiful and Caryn becoming a sleep specialist. As a mother of a heart warrior, Caryn personally understands the emotional impact a scar can have as well as the weight and frustration of being sleep deprived. She is passionate about helping families make sleep easy and turning sleepless nights into peaceful, sweet dreams. Caryn hopes My Scar is Beautiful serves as a positive resource and reminds readers of all the reasons to love their scars!

She can be found online at CarynShender.com

Made in United States
Troutdale, OR
08/14/2024

22003839R00024